FANCY FERNS

16-MONTH LIFESTYLE PLANNER

SEPTEMBER 2022 – DECEMBER 2023

If Lost Please Return To:

SELLERS PUBLISHING

Astronomical information is in Eastern Time and Daylight Saving Time.
Key to abbreviations: United States (US), Canada (CAN), United Kingdom (UK), Australia (AUS), South Australia (SA), Western Australia (W. Australia), New South Wales (NSW), Australian Capital Territory (ACT), New Zealand (NZ).

JANUARY

S	M	T	W	T	F	S
						1
2	3	4	5	6	7	8
9	10	11	12	13	14	15
16	17	18	19	20	21	22
23	24	25	26	27	28	29
30	31					

FEBRUARY

S	M	T	W	T	F	S
		1	2	3	4	5
6	7	8	9	10	11	12
13	14	15	16	17	18	19
20	21	22	23	24	25	26
27	28					

MARCH

S	M	T	W	T	F	S
		1	2	3	4	5
6	7	8	9	10	11	12
13	14	15	16	17	18	19
20	21	22	23	24	25	26
27	28	29	30	31		

APRIL

S	M	T	W	T	F	S
					1	2
3	4	5	6	7	8	9
10	11	12	13	14	15	16
17	18	19	20	21	22	23
24	25	26	27	28	29	30

MAY

S	M	T	W	T	F	S
1	2	3	4	5	6	7
8	9	10	11	12	13	14
15	16	17	18	19	20	21
22	23	24	25	26	27	28
29	30	31				

JUNE

S	M	T	W	T	F	S
			1	2	3	4
5	6	7	8	9	10	11
12	13	14	15	16	17	18
19	20	21	22	23	24	25
26	27	28	29	30		

JULY

S	M	T	W	T	F	S
					1	2
3	4	5	6	7	8	9
10	11	12	13	14	15	16
17	18	19	20	21	22	23
24	25	26	27	28	29	30
31						

AUGUST

S	M	T	W	T	F	S
	1	2	3	4	5	6
7	8	9	10	11	12	13
14	15	16	17	18	19	20
21	22	23	24	25	26	27
28	29	30	31			

SEPTEMBER

S	M	T	W	T	F	S
				1	2	3
4	5	6	7	8	9	10
11	12	13	14	15	16	17
18	19	20	21	22	23	24
25	26	27	28	29	30	

OCTOBER

S	M	T	W	T	F	S
						1
2	3	4	5	6	7	8
9	10	11	12	13	14	15
16	17	18	19	20	21	22
23	24	25	26	27	28	29
30	31					

NOVEMBER

S	M	T	W	T	F	S
		1	2	3	4	5
6	7	8	9	10	11	12
13	14	15	16	17	18	19
20	21	22	23	24	25	26
27	28	29	30			

DECEMBER

S	M	T	W	T	F	S
				1	2	3
4	5	6	7	8	9	10
11	12	13	14	15	16	17
18	19	20	21	22	23	24
25	26	27	28	29	30	31

NOTES

SEPTEMBER 2022

SUNDAY	MONDAY	TUESDAY	WEDNESDAY	THURSDAY	FRIDAY	SATURDAY
AUGUST S M T W T F S 1 2 3 4 5 6 7 8 9 10 11 12 13 14 15 16 17 18 19 20 21 22 23 24 25 26 27 28 29 30 31		OCTOBER S M T W T F S 1 2 3 4 5 6 7 8 9 10 11 12 13 14 15 16 17 18 19 20 21 22 23 24 25 26 27 28 29 30 31	31	1	2	3
4 Father's Day (Australia, NZ)	5 Labor Day (US, Canada)	6	7	8	9	10 ○ FULL MOON
11 Patriot Day	12	13	14	15	16	17
18	19	20	21 UN International Day of Peace	22 Autumnal Equinox	23	24
25 Rosh Hashanah begins at sundown ● NEW MOON	26 Queen's Birthday (W. Australia)	27	28	29	30	1

MONTHLY TO-DO

AUGUST/SEPTEMBER 2022

29
MON

Bank Holiday (UK)

30
TUE

31
WED

1
THU

2
FRI

3
SAT

4
SUN

Father's Day (Australia, NZ)

5
MON

Labor Day (US, Canada)

6
TUE

7
WED

8
THU

9
FRI

10
SAT

○ FULL MOON

11
SUN

Patriot Day

SEPTEMBER 2022

12
MON

13
TUE

14
WED

15
THU

16
FRI

17
SAT

18
SUN

SEPTEMBER 2022

19
MON

20
TUE

21
WED

UN International Day of Peace

22
THU

Autumnal Equinox

23
FRI

24
SAT

25
SUN

Rosh Hashanah begins at sundown
● NEW MOON

26
MON

Queen's Birthday (W. Australia)

27
TUE

28
WED

29
THU

30
FRI

1
SAT

2
SUN

OCTOBER 2022

SUNDAY	MONDAY	TUESDAY	WEDNESDAY	THURSDAY	FRIDAY	SATURDAY
			28	29	30	1
2	3 Labour Day (ACT, NSW, SA) Queen's Birthday (Queensland)	4 Yom Kippur begins at sundown	5	6	7	8
9 ○ FULL MOON	10 Columbus Day (observed) Thanksgiving (Canada) Indigenous Peoples' Day (observed)	11	12	13	14	15
16	17	18	19	20	21	22
23/30	24/31 Labour Day (24th) (New Zealand) Halloween (31st)	25 ● NEW MOON	26	27	28	29

SEPTEMBER

S	M	T	W	T	F	S
				1	2	3
4	5	6	7	8	9	10
11	12	13	14	15	16	17
18	19	20	21	22	23	24
25	26	27	28	29	30	

NOVEMBER

S	M	T	W	T	F	S
		1	2	3	4	5
6	7	8	9	10	11	12
13	14	15	16	17	18	19
20	21	22	23	24	25	26
27	28	29	30			

MONTHLY TO-DO

OCTOBER 2022

3
MON

Labour Day (ACT, NSW, SA)
Queen's Birthday (Queensland)

4
TUE

Yom Kippur begins at sundown

5
WED

6
THU

7
FRI

8
SAT

9
SUN

○ FULL MOON

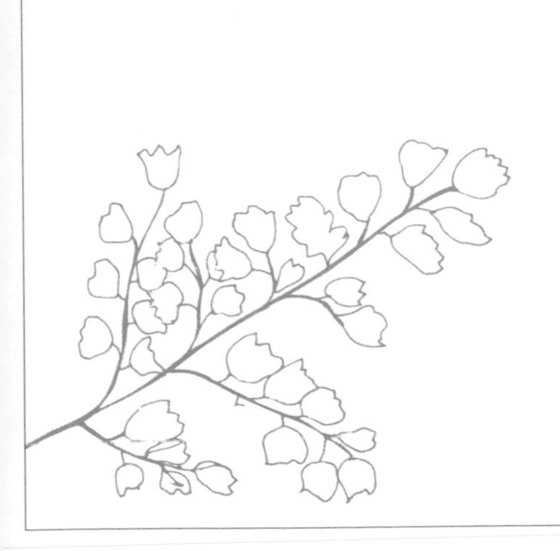

OCTOBER 2022

10
MON

Columbus Day (observed)
Thanksgiving (Canada)
Indigenous Peoples' Day (observed)

11
TUE

12
WED

13
THU

14
FRI

15
SAT

16
SUN

OCTOBER 2022

17
MON

18
TUE

19
WED

20
THU

21
FRI

22
SAT

23
SUN

OCTOBER 2022

24
MON

Labour Day (New Zealand)

25
TUE

● NEW MOON

26
WED

27
THU

28
FRI

29
SAT

30
SUN

NOVEMBER 2022

SUNDAY	MONDAY	TUESDAY	WEDNESDAY	THURSDAY	FRIDAY	SATURDAY
30	31	1 All Saints' Day	2	3	4	5
6 Daylight Saving ends	7	8 Election Day ○ FULL MOON	9	10	11 Veterans Day Remembrance Day (CAN, AUS, NZ)	12
13 Remembrance Sunday (UK)	14	15	16	17	18	19
20	21	22	23 ● NEW MOON	24 Thanksgiving	25	26
27	28	29	30			

OCTOBER

S	M	T	W	T	F	S
						1
2	3	4	5	6	7	8
9	10	11	12	13	14	15
16	17	18	19	20	21	22
23	24	25	26	27	28	29
30	31					

DECEMBER

S	M	T	W	T	F	S
				1	2	3
4	5	6	7	8	9	10
11	12	13	14	15	16	17
18	19	20	21	22	23	24
25	26	27	28	29	30	31

MONTHLY TO-DO

OCTOBER/NOVEMBER 2022

31
MON

Halloween

1
TUE

All Saints' Day

2
WED

3
THU

4
FRI

5
SAT

6
SUN

Daylight Saving ends

7
MON

8
TUE

Election Day
○ FULL MOON

9
WED

10
THU

11
FRI

Veterans Day
Remembrance Day (CAN, AUS, NZ)

12
SAT

13
SUN

Remembrance Sunday (UK)

NOVEMBER 2022

14
MON

15
TUE

16
WED

17
THU

18
FRI

19
SAT

20
SUN

NOVEMBER 2022

21
MON

22
TUE

23
WED

● NEW MOON

24
THU

Thanksgiving

25
FRI

26
SAT

27
SUN

NOVEMBER/DECEMBER 2022

28
MON

29
TUE

30
WED

1
THU

2
FRI

3
SAT

4
SUN

DECEMBER 2022

SUNDAY	MONDAY	TUESDAY	WEDNESDAY	THURSDAY	FRIDAY	SATURDAY
			30	1	2	3
4	5	6	7 Pearl Harbor Remembrance Day ○ FULL MOON	8	9	10
11	12	13	14	15	16	17
18 Hanukkah begins at sundown	19	20	21 Winter Solstice	22	23 ● NEW MOON	24
25 Christmas	26 Boxing Day (CAN, UK, AUS, NZ) Kwanzaa begins	27	28	29	30	31

NOVEMBER

S	M	T	W	T	F	S
		1	2	3	4	5
6	7	8	9	10	11	12
13	14	15	16	17	18	19
20	21	22	23	24	25	26
27	28	29	30			

JANUARY 2023

S	M	T	W	T	F	S
1	2	3	4	5	6	7
8	9	10	11	12	13	14
15	16	17	18	19	20	21
22	23	24	25	26	27	28
29	30	31				

MONTHLY TO-DO

- [ ]
- [ ]
- [ ]
- [ ]
- [ ]
- [ ]
- [ ]
- [ ]
- [ ]
- [ ]
- [ ]
- [ ]
- [ ]
- [ ]
- [ ]
- [ ]
- [ ]
- [ ]

DECEMBER 2022

5
MON

6
TUE

7
WED

Pearl Harbor Remembrance Day
○ FULL MOON

8
THU

9
FRI

10
SAT

11
SUN

DECEMBER 2022

12
MON

13
TUE

14
WED

15
THU

16
FRI

17
SAT

18
SUN

Hanukkah begins at sundown

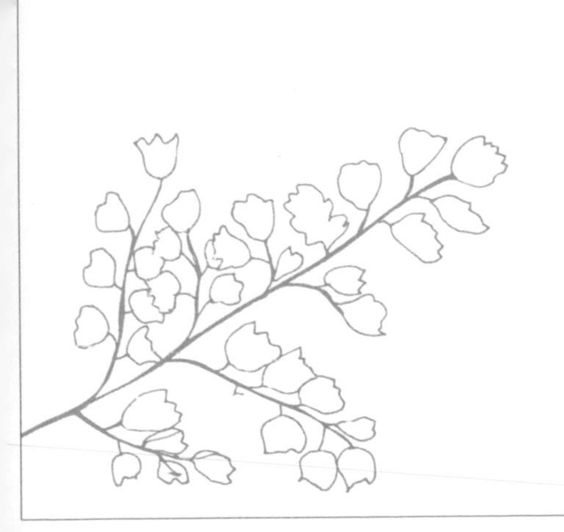

DECEMBER 2022

19
MON

20
TUE

21
WED

Winter Solstice

22
THU

23
FRI

● NEW MOON

24
SAT

25
SUN

Christmas

26
MON

Boxing Day (CAN, UK, AUS, NZ)
Kwanzaa begins

27
TUE

28
WED

29
THU

30
FRI

31
SAT

1
SUN

New Year's Day

JANUARY

S	M	T	W	T	F	S
1	2	3	4	5	6	7
8	9	10	11	12	13	14
15	16	17	18	19	20	21
22	23	24	25	26	27	28
29	30	31				

FEBRUARY

S	M	T	W	T	F	S
			1	2	3	4
5	6	7	8	9	10	11
12	13	14	15	16	17	18
19	20	21	22	23	24	25
26	27	28				

MARCH

S	M	T	W	T	F	S
			1	2	3	4
5	6	7	8	9	10	11
12	13	14	15	16	17	18
19	20	21	22	23	24	25
26	27	28	29	30	31	

APRIL

S	M	T	W	T	F	S
						1
2	3	4	5	6	7	8
9	10	11	12	13	14	15
16	17	18	19	20	21	22
23	24	25	26	27	28	29
30						

MAY

S	M	T	W	T	F	S
	1	2	3	4	5	6
7	8	9	10	11	12	13
14	15	16	17	18	19	20
21	22	23	24	25	26	27
28	29	30	31			

JUNE

S	M	T	W	T	F	S
				1	2	3
4	5	6	7	8	9	10
11	12	13	14	15	16	17
18	19	20	21	22	23	24
25	26	27	28	29	30	

JULY

S	M	T	W	T	F	S
						1
2	3	4	5	6	7	8
9	10	11	12	13	14	15
16	17	18	19	20	21	22
23	24	25	26	27	28	29
30	31					

AUGUST

S	M	T	W	T	F	S
		1	2	3	4	5
6	7	8	9	10	11	12
13	14	15	16	17	18	19
20	21	22	23	24	25	26
27	28	29	30	31		

SEPTEMBER

S	M	T	W	T	F	S
					1	2
3	4	5	6	7	8	9
10	11	12	13	14	15	16
17	18	19	20	21	22	23
24	25	26	27	28	29	30

OCTOBER

S	M	T	W	T	F	S
1	2	3	4	5	6	7
8	9	10	11	12	13	14
15	16	17	18	19	20	21
22	23	24	25	26	27	28
29	30	31				

NOVEMBER

S	M	T	W	T	F	S
			1	2	3	4
5	6	7	8	9	10	11
12	13	14	15	16	17	18
19	20	21	22	23	24	25
26	27	28	29	30		

DECEMBER

S	M	T	W	T	F	S
					1	2
3	4	5	6	7	8	9
10	11	12	13	14	15	16
17	18	19	20	21	22	23
24	25	26	27	28	29	30
31						

NOTES

JANUARY 2023

SUNDAY	MONDAY	TUESDAY	WEDNESDAY	THURSDAY	FRIDAY	SATURDAY
1 New Year's Day	2	3	4	5	6 ○ FULL MOON	7
8	9	10	11	12	13	14
15 Martin Luther King Jr.'s Birthday	16 Martin Luther King Jr.'s Birthday (observed)	17	18	19	20	21 ● NEW MOON
22 Chinese New Year	23	24	25	26 Australia Day	27	28
29	30	31	1			

DECEMBER 2022

S	M	T	W	T	F	S
				1	2	3
4	5	6	7	8	9	10
11	12	13	14	15	16	17
18	19	20	21	22	23	24
25	26	27	28	29	30	31

FEBRUARY

S	M	T	W	T	F	S
			1	2	3	4
5	6	7	8	9	10	11
12	13	14	15	16	17	18
19	20	21	22	23	24	25
26	27	28				

MONTHLY TO-DO

JANUARY 2023

2
MON

3
TUE

4
WED

5
THU

6
FRI

○ FULL MOON

7
SAT

8
SUN

JANUARY 2023

9
MON

10
TUE

11
WED

12
THU

13
FRI

14
SAT

15
SUN

Martin Luther King Jr.'s Birthday

16
MON

Martin Luther King Jr.'s Birthday (observed)

17
TUE

18
WED

19
THU

20
FRI

21
SAT

● NEW MOON

22
SUN

Chinese New Year

23
MON

24
TUE

25
WED

26
THU

Australia Day

27
FRI

28
SAT

29
SUN

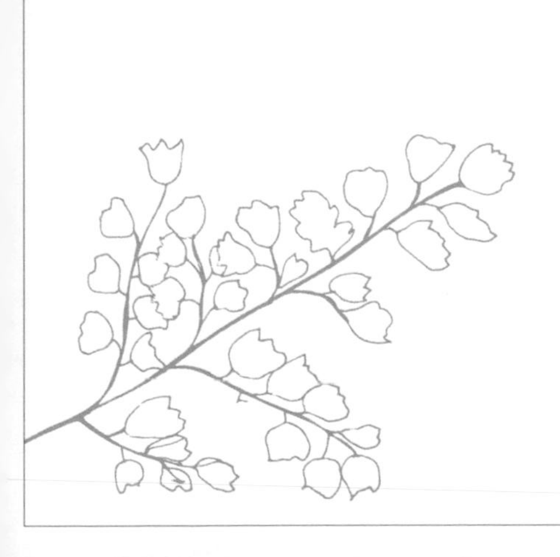

FEBRUARY 2023

SUNDAY	MONDAY	TUESDAY	WEDNESDAY	THURSDAY	FRIDAY	SATURDAY
29	30	31	1	2 Groundhog Day	3	4
5 ○ FULL MOON	6 Waitangi Day (New Zealand)	7	8	9	10	11
12 Lincoln's Birthday	13	14 Valentine's Day	15	16	17	18
19	20 Presidents' Day ● NEW MOON	21	22 Washington's Birthday Ash Wednesday	23	24	25
26	27	28	1			

JANUARY

S	M	T	W	T	F	S
1	2	3	4	5	6	7
8	9	10	11	12	13	14
15	16	17	18	19	20	21
22	23	24	25	26	27	28
29	30	31				

MARCH

S	M	T	W	T	F	S
			1	2	3	4
5	6	7	8	9	10	11
12	13	14	15	16	17	18
19	20	21	22	23	24	25
26	27	28	29	30	31	

MONTHLY TO-DO

JANUARY/FEBRUARY 2023

30
MON

31
TUE

1
WED

2
THU

Groundhog Day

3
FRI

4
SAT

5
SUN

○ FULL MOON

6
MON

Waitangi Day (New Zealand)

7
TUE

8
WED

9
THU

10
FRI

11
SAT

12
SUN

Lincoln's Birthday

FEBRUARY 2023

13
MON

14
TUE

Valentine's Day

15
WED

16
THU

17
FRI

18
SAT

19
SUN

FEBRUARY 2023

20
MON

Presidents' Day
● NEW MOON

21
TUE

22
WED

Washington's Birthday
Ash Wednesday

23
THU

24
FRI

25
SAT

26
SUN

MARCH 2023

SUNDAY	MONDAY	TUESDAY	WEDNESDAY	THURSDAY	FRIDAY	SATURDAY
FEBRUARY S M T W T F S 1 2 3 4 5 6 7 8 9 10 11 12 13 14 15 16 17 18 19 20 21 22 23 24 25 26 27 28	APRIL S M T W T F S 1 2 3 4 5 6 7 8 9 10 11 12 13 14 15 16 17 18 19 20 21 22 23 24 25 26 27 28 29 30		1	2	3	4
5	6 Labour Day (W. Australia)	7 ○ FULL MOON	8 International Women's Day	9	10	11
12 Daylight Saving begins	13 Commonwealth Day (CAN, UK, Australia) Canberra Day (ACT) Labour Day (Victoria)	14	15	16	17 St. Patrick's Day	18
19 Mother's Day (UK)	20 Vernal Equinox	21 ● NEW MOON	22	23	24	25
26	27	28	29	30	31	1

MONTHLY TO-DO

27
MON

28
TUE

1
WED

2
THU

3
FRI

4
SAT

5
SUN

6
MON

Labour Day (W. Australia)

7
TUE

○ FULL MOON

8
WED

International Women's Day

9
THU

10
FRI

11
SAT

12
SUN

Daylight Saving begins

13
MON

Commonwealth Day (CAN, UK, Australia)
Canberra Day (ACT)
Labour Day (Victoria)

14
TUE

15
WED

16
THU

17
FRI

St. Patrick's Day

18
SAT

19
SUN

Mother's Day (UK)

MARCH 2023

20
MON

Vernal Equinox

21
TUE

● NEW MOON

22
WED

23
THU

24
FRI

25
SAT

26
SUN

27
MON

28
TUE

29
WED

30
THU

31
FRI

1
SAT

2
SUN

Palm Sunday

APRIL 2023

SUNDAY	MONDAY	TUESDAY	WEDNESDAY	THURSDAY	FRIDAY	SATURDAY
			29	30	31	1
2 Palm Sunday	3	4	5 Passover begins at sundown	6 ○ FULL MOON	7 Good Friday	8
9 Easter Sunday	10 Easter Monday (CAN, UK, AUS, NZ)	11	12	13	14	15
16	17 Holocaust Remembrance Day begins at sundown	18	19	20 ● NEW MOON	21	22 Earth Day
23/30	24	25 ANZAC Day (Australia, NZ)	26	27	28 Arbor Day	29

MARCH

S	M	T	W	T	F	S
			1	2	3	4
5	6	7	8	9	10	11
12	13	14	15	16	17	18
19	20	21	22	23	24	25
26	27	28	29	30	31	

MAY

S	M	T	W	T	F	S
	1	2	3	4	5	6
7	8	9	10	11	12	13
14	15	16	17	18	19	20
21	22	23	24	25	26	27
28	29	30	31			

MONTHLY TO-DO

APRIL 2023

3
MON

4
TUE

5
WED

Passover begins at sundown

6
THU

○ FULL MOON

7
FRI

Good Friday

8
SAT

9
SUN

Easter Sunday

10
MON

Easter Monday (CAN, UK, AUS, NZ)

11
TUE

12
WED

13
THU

14
FRI

15
SAT

16
SUN

APRIL 2023

17
MON

Holocaust Remembrance Day
begins at sundown

18
TUE

19
WED

20
THU

● NEW MOON

21
FRI

22
SAT

Earth Day

23
SUN

24
MON

25
TUE

ANZAC Day (Australia, NZ)

26
WED

27
THU

28
FRI

Arbor Day

29
SAT

30
SUN

MAY 2023

SUNDAY	MONDAY	TUESDAY	WEDNESDAY	THURSDAY	FRIDAY	SATURDAY
30	1 May Day Bank Holiday (UK) Labour Day (Queensland)	2	3	4	5 ○ FULL MOON	6
7	8	9	10	11	12	13
14 Mother's Day (US, CAN, AUS, NZ)	15	16	17	18	19 ● NEW MOON	20 Armed Forces Day
21	22 Victoria Day (Canada)	23	24	25	26	27
28	29 Memorial Day Bank Holiday (UK)	30	31			

APRIL

S	M	T	W	T	F	S
						1
2	3	4	5	6	7	8
9	10	11	12	13	14	15
16	17	18	19	20	21	22
23	24	25	26	27	28	29
30						

JUNE

S	M	T	W	T	F	S
				1	2	3
4	5	6	7	8	9	10
11	12	13	14	15	16	17
18	19	20	21	22	23	24
25	26	27	28	29	30	

MONTHLY TO-DO

MAY 2023

1
MON

May Day
Bank Holiday (UK)
Labour Day (Queensland)

2
TUE

3
WED

4
THU

5
FRI

○ FULL MOON

6
SAT

7
SUN

8
MON

9
TUE

10
WED

11
THU

12
FRI

13
SAT

14
SUN

Mother's Day (US, CAN, AUS, NZ)

MAY 2023

15
MON

16
TUE

17
WED

18
THU

19
FRI

● NEW MOON

20
SAT

Armed Forces Day

21
SUN

22
MON

Victoria Day (Canada)

23
TUE

24
WED

25
THU

26
FRI

27
SAT

28
SUN

MAY / JUNE 2023

29
MON

Memorial Day
Bank Holiday (UK)

30
TUE

31
WED

1
THU

2
FRI

3
SAT

○ FULL MOON

4
SUN

JUNE 2023

SUNDAY	MONDAY	TUESDAY	WEDNESDAY	THURSDAY	FRIDAY	SATURDAY
			31	1	2	3 ○ FULL MOON
4	5 Queen's Birthday (New Zealand)	6	7	8	9	10
11	12 Queen's Birthday (Australia)	13	14 Flag Day	15	16	17
18 Father's Day (US, Canada, UK) ● NEW MOON	19 Juneteenth	20	21 Summer Solstice	22	23	24
25	26	27	28	29	30	1

MAY

S	M	T	W	T	F	S
	1	2	3	4	5	6
7	8	9	10	11	12	13
14	15	16	17	18	19	20
21	22	23	24	25	26	27
28	29	30	31			

JULY

S	M	T	W	T	F	S
						1
2	3	4	5	6	7	8
9	10	11	12	13	14	15
16	17	18	19	20	21	22
23	24	25	26	27	28	29
30	31					

MONTHLY TO-DO

JUNE 2023

5
MON

Queen's Birthday (New Zealand)

6
TUE

7
WED

8
THU

9
FRI

10
SAT

11
SUN

12
MON

Queen's Birthday (Australia)

13
TUE

14
WED

Flag Day

15
THU

16
FRI

17
SAT

18
SUN

Father's Day (US, Canada, UK)
● NEW MOON

JUNE 2023

19
MON

Juneteenth

20
TUE

21
WED

Summer Solstice

22
THU

23
FRI

24
SAT

25
SUN

JUNE/JULY 2023

26
MON

27
TUE

28
WED

29
THU

30
FRI

1
SAT

Canada Day

2
SUN

JULY 2023

SUNDAY	MONDAY	TUESDAY	WEDNESDAY	THURSDAY	FRIDAY	SATURDAY
			28	29	30	1 Canada Day
2	3 ○ FULL MOON	4 Independence Day	5	6	7	8
9	10	11	12	13	14	15
16	17 ● NEW MOON	18	19	20	21	22
23/30	24/31	25	26	27	28	29

JUNE

S	M	T	W	T	F	S
				1	2	3
4	5	6	7	8	9	10
11	12	13	14	15	16	17
18	19	20	21	22	23	24
25	26	27	28	29	30	

AUGUST

S	M	T	W	T	F	S
		1	2	3	4	5
6	7	8	9	10	11	12
13	14	15	16	17	18	19
20	21	22	23	24	25	26
27	28	29	30	31		

MONTHLY TO-DO

JULY 2023

3
MON

○ FULL MOON

4
TUE

Independence Day

5
WED

6
THU

7
FRI

8
SAT

9
SUN

10
MON

11
TUE

12
WED

13
THU

14
FRI

15
SAT

16
SUN

17
MON

● NEW MOON

18
TUE

19
WED

20
THU

21
FRI

22
SAT

23
SUN

JULY 2023

24
MON

25
TUE

26
WED

27
THU

28
FRI

29
SAT

30
SUN

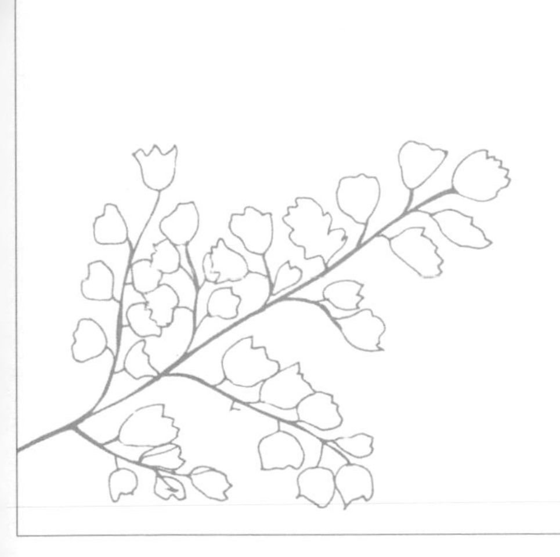

AUGUST 2023

SUNDAY	MONDAY	TUESDAY	WEDNESDAY	THURSDAY	FRIDAY	SATURDAY
		1 ○ FULL MOON	2	3	4	5
6	7 Civic Holiday (Canada) Bank Holiday (NSW)	8	9	10	11	12
13	14	15	16 ● NEW MOON	17	18	19
20	21	22	23	24	25	26
27	28 Bank Holiday (UK)	29	30 ○ FULL MOON	31		

JULY

S	M	T	W	T	F	S
						1
2	3	4	5	6	7	8
9	10	11	12	13	14	15
16	17	18	19	20	21	22
23	24	25	26	27	28	29
30	31					

SEPTEMBER

S	M	T	W	T	F	S
					1	2
3	4	5	6	7	8	9
10	11	12	13	14	15	16
17	18	19	20	21	22	23
24	25	26	27	28	29	30

MONTHLY TO-DO

JULY/AUGUST 2023

31
MON

1
TUE

○ FULL MOON

2
WED

3
THU

4
FRI

5
SAT

6
SUN

AUGUST 2023

7
MON

Civic Holiday (Canada)
Bank Holiday (NSW)

8
TUE

9
WED

10
THU

11
FRI

12
SAT

13
SUN

AUGUST 2023

14
MON

15
TUE

16
WED

● NEW MOON

17
THU

18
FRI

19
SAT

20
SUN

AUGUST 2023

21
MON

22
TUE

23
WED

24
THU

25
FRI

26
SAT

27
SUN

AUGUST/SEPTEMBER 2023

28
MON

Bank Holiday (UK)

29
TUE

30
WED

○ FULL MOON

31
THU

1
FRI

2
SAT

3
SUN

Father's Day (Australia, NZ)

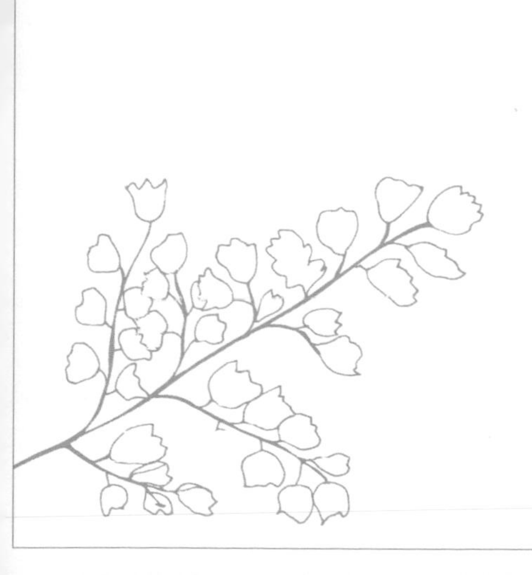

SEPTEMBER 2023

SUNDAY	MONDAY	TUESDAY	WEDNESDAY	THURSDAY	FRIDAY	SATURDAY
			30	31	1	2
3 Father's Day (Australia, NZ)	4 Labor Day (US, Canada)	5	6	7	8	9
10	11 Patriot Day	12	13	14 ● NEW MOON	15 Rosh Hashanah begins at sundown	16
17	18	19	20	21 UN International Day of Peace	22	23 Autumnal Equinox
24 Yom Kippur begins at sundown	25 Queen's Birthday (W. Australia)	26	27	28	29 ○ FULL MOON	30

AUGUST

S	M	T	W	T	F	S
		1	2	3	4	5
6	7	8	9	10	11	12
13	14	15	16	17	18	19
20	21	22	23	24	25	26
27	28	29	30	31		

OCTOBER

S	M	T	W	T	F	S
1	2	3	4	5	6	7
8	9	10	11	12	13	14
15	16	17	18	19	20	21
22	23	24	25	26	27	28
29	30	31				

MONTHLY TO-DO

SEPTEMBER 2023

4
MON

Labor Day (US, Canada)

5
TUE

6
WED

7
THU

8
FRI

9
SAT

10
SUN

SEPTEMBER 2023

11
MON

Patriot Day

12
TUE

13
WED

14
THU

● NEW MOON

15
FRI

Rosh Hashanah begins at sundown

16
SAT

17
SUN

SEPTEMBER 2023

18
MON

19
TUE

20
WED

21
THU

UN International Day of Peace

22
FRI

23
SAT

Autumnal Equinox

24
SUN

Yom Kippur begins at sundown

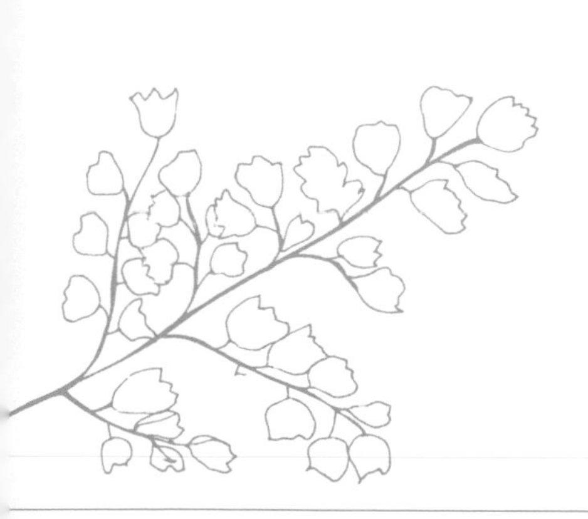

SEPTEMBER/OCTOBER 2023

25
MON

Queen's Birthday (W. Australia)

26
TUE

27
WED

28
THU

29
FRI

○ FULL MOON

30
SAT

1
SUN

OCTOBER 2023

SUNDAY	MONDAY	TUESDAY	WEDNESDAY	THURSDAY	FRIDAY	SATURDAY
1	2 Labour Day (ACT, NSW, SA) Queen's Birthday (Queensland)	3	4	5	6	7
8	9 Columbus Day (observed) Thanksgiving (Canada) Indigenous Peoples' Day (observed)	10	11	12	13	14 ● NEW MOON
15	16	17	18	19	20	21
22	23 Labour Day (New Zealand)	24	25	26	27	28 ○ FULL MOON
29	30	31 Halloween	1			

SEPTEMBER

S	M	T	W	T	F	S
					1	2
3	4	5	6	7	8	9
10	11	12	13	14	15	16
17	18	19	20	21	22	23
24	25	26	27	28	29	30

NOVEMBER

S	M	T	W	T	F	S
			1	2	3	4
5	6	7	8	9	10	11
12	13	14	15	16	17	18
19	20	21	22	23	24	25
26	27	28	29	30		

MONTHLY TO-DO

OCTOBER 2023

2
MON

Labour Day (ACT, NSW, SA)
Queen's Birthday (Queensland)

3
TUE

4
WED

5
THU

6
FRI

7
SAT

8
SUN

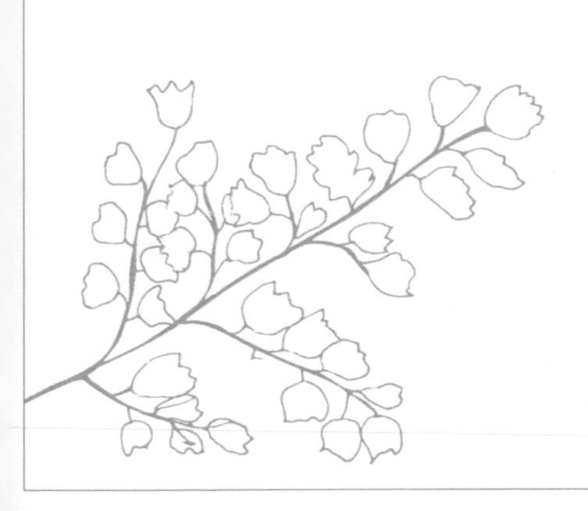

OCTOBER 2023

9
MON

Columbus Day (observed)
Thanksgiving (Canada)
Indigenous Peoples' Day (observed)

10
TUE

11
WED

12
THU

13
FRI

14
SAT

● NEW MOON

15
SUN

OCTOBER 2023

16
MON

17
TUE

18
WED

19
THU

20
FRI

21
SAT

22
SUN

23
MON

Labour Day (New Zealand)

24
TUE

25
WED

26
THU

27
FRI

28
SAT

○ FULL MOON

29
SUN

NOVEMBER 2023

SUNDAY	MONDAY	TUESDAY	WEDNESDAY	THURSDAY	FRIDAY	SATURDAY
OCTOBER S M T W T F S 1 2 3 4 5 6 7 8 9 10 11 12 13 14 15 16 17 18 19 20 21 22 23 24 25 26 27 28 29 30 31	DECEMBER S M T W T F S 1 2 3 4 5 6 7 8 9 10 11 12 13 14 15 16 17 18 19 20 21 22 23 24 25 26 27 28 29 30 31		1 All Saints' Day	2	3	4
5 Daylight Saving ends	6	7 Election Day	8	9	10	11 Veterans Day Remembrance Day (CAN, AUS, NZ)
12 Remembrance Sunday (UK)	13 ● NEW MOON	14	15	16	17	18
19	20	21	22	23 Thanksgiving	24	25
26	27 ○ FULL MOON	28	29	30	1	2

MONTHLY TO-DO

OCTOBER/NOVEMBER 2023

30
MON

31
TUE

Halloween

1
WED

All Saints' Day

2
THU

3
FRI

4
SAT

5
SUN

Daylight Saving ends

NOVEMBER 2023

6
MON

7
TUE

Election Day

8
WED

9
THU

10
FRI

11
SAT

Veterans Day
Remembrance Day (CAN, AUS, NZ)

12
SUN

Remembrance Sunday (UK)

NOVEMBER 2023

13
MON

● NEW MOON

14
TUE

15
WED

16
THU

17
FRI

18
SAT

19
SUN

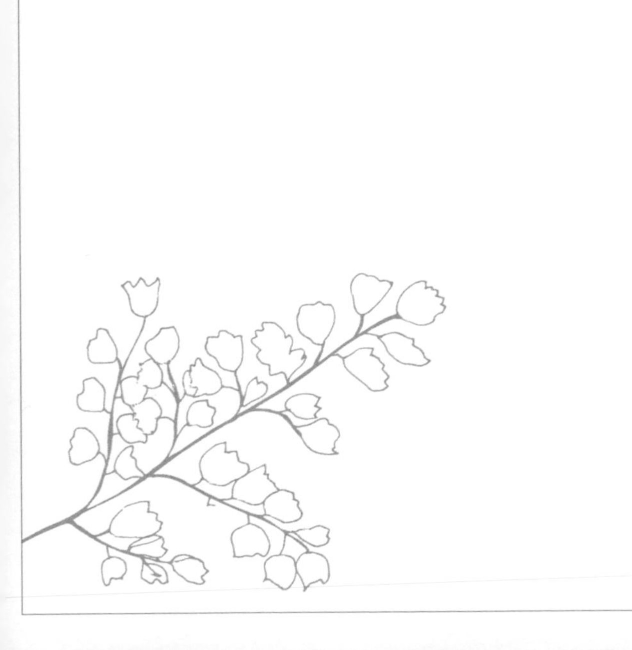

NOVEMBER 2023

20
MON

21
TUE

22
WED

23
THU

Thanksgiving

24
FRI

25
SAT

26
SUN

NOVEMBER/DECEMBER 2023

27
MON

○ FULL MOON

28
TUE

29
WED

30
THU

1
FRI

2
SAT

3
SUN

DECEMBER 2023

SUNDAY	MONDAY	TUESDAY	WEDNESDAY	THURSDAY	FRIDAY	SATURDAY
			29	30	1	2
3	4	5	6	7 Pearl Harbor Remembrance Day Hanukkah begins at sundown	8	9
10	11	12 ● NEW MOON	13	14	15	16
17	18	19	20	21 Winter Solstice	22	23
24/31	25 Christmas	26 Boxing Day (CAN, UK, AUS, NZ) Kwanzaa begins ○ FULL MOON	27	28	29	30

NOVEMBER

S	M	T	W	T	F	S
			1	2	3	4
5	6	7	8	9	10	11
12	13	14	15	16	17	18
19	20	21	22	23	24	25
26	27	28	29	30		

JANUARY 2024

S	M	T	W	T	F	S
	1	2	3	4	5	6
7	8	9	10	11	12	13
14	15	16	17	18	19	20
21	22	23	24	25	26	27
28	29	30	31			

MONTHLY TO-DO

DECEMBER 2023

4
MON

5
TUE

6
WED

7
THU

Pearl Harbor Remembrance Day
Hanukkah begins at sundown

8
FRI

9
SAT

10
SUN

DECEMBER 2023

11
MON

12
TUE

● NEW MOON

13
WED

14
THU

15
FRI

16
SAT

17
SUN

DECEMBER 2023

18
MON

19
TUE

20
WED

21
THU

Winter Solstice

22
FRI

23
SAT

24
SUN

25
MON

Christmas

26
TUE

Boxing Day (CAN, UK, AUS, NZ)
Kwanzaa begins
○ FULL MOON

27
WED

28
THU

29
FRI

30
SAT

31
SUN

JANUARY

S	M	T	W	T	F	S
	1	2	3	4	5	6
7	8	9	10	11	12	13
14	15	16	17	18	19	20
21	22	23	24	25	26	27
28	29	30	31			

FEBRUARY

S	M	T	W	T	F	S
				1	2	3
4	5	6	7	8	9	10
11	12	13	14	15	16	17
18	19	20	21	22	23	24
25	26	27	28	29		

MARCH

S	M	T	W	T	F	S
					1	2
3	4	5	6	7	8	9
10	11	12	13	14	15	16
17	18	19	20	21	22	23
24	25	26	27	28	29	30
31						

APRIL

S	M	T	W	T	F	S
	1	2	3	4	5	6
7	8	9	10	11	12	13
14	15	16	17	18	19	20
21	22	23	24	25	26	27
28	29	30				

MAY

S	M	T	W	T	F	S
			1	2	3	4
5	6	7	8	9	10	11
12	13	14	15	16	17	18
19	20	21	22	23	24	25
26	27	28	29	30	31	

JUNE

S	M	T	W	T	F	S
						1
2	3	4	5	6	7	8
9	10	11	12	13	14	15
16	17	18	19	20	21	22
23	24	25	26	27	28	29
30						

JULY

S	M	T	W	T	F	S
	1	2	3	4	5	6
7	8	9	10	11	12	13
14	15	16	17	18	19	20
21	22	23	24	25	26	27
28	29	30	31			

AUGUST

S	M	T	W	T	F	S
				1	2	3
4	5	6	7	8	9	10
11	12	13	14	15	16	17
18	19	20	21	22	23	24
25	26	27	28	29	30	31

SEPTEMBER

S	M	T	W	T	F	S
1	2	3	4	5	6	7
8	9	10	11	12	13	14
15	16	17	18	19	20	21
22	23	24	25	26	27	28
29	30					

OCTOBER

S	M	T	W	T	F	S
		1	2	3	4	5
6	7	8	9	10	11	12
13	14	15	16	17	18	19
20	21	22	23	24	25	26
27	28	29	30	31		

NOVEMBER

S	M	T	W	T	F	S
					1	2
3	4	5	6	7	8	9
10	11	12	13	14	15	16
17	18	19	20	21	22	23
24	25	26	27	28	29	30

DECEMBER

S	M	T	W	T	F	S
1	2	3	4	5	6	7
8	9	10	11	12	13	14
15	16	17	18	19	20	21
22	23	24	25	26	27	28
29	30	31				

NOTES

For more information
regarding this and other products:
WWW.MAKEFUN.COM | RSP@RSVP.COM

Canadian Stores Contact: Andrew Shapiro
(800) 625-3386 | ASHAPIRO@RSVP.COM

ISBN 13: 978-1-5319-1758-6
Printed in China with soy-based inks.